Kim Woodworth
11·19·08

DAYICAN PUBLISHING, 2008

Copyright © 2008 by Kim Woodworth

today I can
Do Anything

By Kim Woodworth

Illustrated by Alexis Gastwirth

For Hunter, Ben, and Sarah, who can do ANYTHING!

Today I can do anything!

Today I'll eat spinach when taking my bath

Today I'll hop on one leg while singing a song

I'll ride my bike while in my pajamas

I'll be nice to my mother
and sister and brother

I'll go shopping with dad and not ask for a thing...

Well, maybe a toy, or a parrot, or ring!

Today I can do anything!

Today I can jump 10 feet in the air

Today I can run as fast as a bear!

Today I can whistle and skip and swim

Today's a great day; I hope you'll join in!

Today I can do anything!

Today I'll eat pudding and broccoli and beans!

BbCcDdEeFfGgHhIiJjK

Today I'll do whatever I can

$$2 + 1 = 3$$
$$1 + 1 = 2$$

Today I'll play in a big brass band!

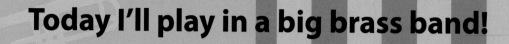

Today I can do anything!

What would you like to do today?